W9-CHF-754

Truly.
Jan Wahl

Ju
221.95
W12   Wahl, Jan.
a   Runaway Jonah, and
       other tales.

Temple Israel

Library

Minneapolis, Minn.

Please sign your full name on the above
card.

Return books promptly to the Library or
Temple Office.

Fines will be charged for overdue books
or for damage or loss of same.

LIBRARY BUREAU CAT. NO. 1166.3

RUNAWAY JONAH

AND OTHER TALES

RUNAWAY JONAH
and other tales

BY JAN WAHL
pictures by uri shulevitz

THE MACMILLAN COMPANY, NEW YORK

Ju
221.95
W12
a

FOR HARRIET
THE MUSIC-MAKER

Copyright © Jan Wahl 1968
Copyright © Uri Shulevitz 1968
All rights reserved. No part of this book may be
reproduced or transmitted in any form or by any means,
electronic or mechanical, including photocopying,
recording or by any information storage and retrieval system,
without permission in writing from the Publisher.
The Macmillan Company, New York
Collier-Macmillan Canada, Ltd., Toronto, Ontario
Library of Congress catalog card number: 68-12084
Printed in the United States of America

FIRST PRINTING

69-57   2-26-69   SSG   395/316

CONTENTS

GOOD DANIEL

THIS is the story of Daniel. Now Daniel was a wise good young man and fair of face.

He had three friends, Shadrach the carpenter, Meshach the gardener, and Abed-nego the poultryman.

Shadrach, Meshach, and Abed-nego were not getting along with the king very well. So one day the king made them go into the fiery furnace with their Sunday coats on.

1

The king shouted, "That will fix them."

Poor Shadrach, Meshach, and Abed-nego walked around in the middle of the fiery furnace with their Sunday coats on. Flames flew, the smoke rolled, the coals were red-hot. There was a sharp crackling and sizzling. Still, they just kept walking around with their coats on.

Soon, somebody ran to tell the king. "King, look. Even their beards aren't singed. They are just talking to their best friend, Daniel." Now the king had to see *that*.

"They are special," he said. "Anybody can see that. And I do not want them in the fiery furnace any more."

So Daniel was able to bring them out. Then they all had a feast of roast chicken brought by Abed-nego, on a table built by Shadrach, with lilies and pinks picked by Meshach. And they were able to take their Sunday coats off.

It was another time. The sun was shining and the insects were sunning themselves on the ground.

Somebody got Daniel into trouble; there were a lot of troublemakers around in those days.

And Daniel was delivered into the lions' pit.

Once he was in the pit, they took away the ladder. The lions were running back and forth, searching for scraps, because they were very hungry and thin.

By then there was another king, one who had a long and curly beard. The king went to sleep on his couch of satin and silk and in the morning he asked, "How did Daniel get along?"

"He got along with the lions fine," somebody said. The king decided he had to see THAT, and rushed down before breakfast.

"Let him out," bellowed the king. "He is somebody special, which anybody can see."

So they threw the real troublemakers down to the lions, while Daniel got taken home on a camel.

One night, Daniel had a dream—in which he saw God shining like a great lamp right in front of him. And he kneeled before God and was strong and twice as wise as before.

Next, he dreamed he was climbing an oak tree straight to Heaven, a place made of polished silver and glowing gold.

There the angels, shining with white robes, showed him the Lion Eagle, and the Bear Who Eats Shortribs, and the Flying Leopard, and the

4

last beast of all, the Beast With Ten Horns. And
Daniel spoke to each of them, one after the other,
knowing it was but a wonderful dream. And the
beasts told him the secrets of Heaven and he listened.

Then he climbed back down the tree to his rough
bed of dry leaves.

And he awoke happy and warm.

SELAH

CAPTAIN NOAH

ONCE there was an old man, six hundred years old. His name was Noah. Noah lived with his old wife in a faded blue tent by a granite mountain.

Nearby lived his three sons, Shem and Ham and Japheth, who'd married three pretty and clever ladies. All of them worked hard picking tender grapes in the vineyards. They knew they mustn't work on the Sabbath. And the sons were very good about visiting their father and mother regularly.

7

At sunrise, the whole family would kneel together in the cool grasses at the foot of the mountain, praying to the Lord. The Lord was pleased.

The Lord, however, was not pleased with the rest of the people, who were robbing and making wars and dancing wildly every night. Something ought to be done about this, decided the Lord.

So the next time Noah was gazing up into the sky, the Lord spoke in a loud but gentle voice.

"MAKE AN ARK. HERE ARE THE PLANS." (And the Lord told him how to make it.) "FOR THERE WILL SOON BE A FLOOD—SO YOU MUST GATHER TWO OF EVERY FISH, BEAST, AND FOWL. AND OF COURSE MRS. NOAH MUST PREPARE PLENTY OF FOOD. YOU WILL BE SAVED, IF YOU STAY ON THIS ARK."

"I will stay on the Ark," promised Noah. Then and there Noah started, with his sons, to build an Ark out of gopher wood and tar.

Everybody laughed at Noah and his sons and wives being so busy instead of having a good time. However, Noah knew what he was doing.

Then, when they had a fine Ark, Noah and his sons went out to gather up the fishes, beasts, and fowls. It was not easy. But they worked very hard at it.

8

Two by two they came into the Ark, big and small. The panthers, who were swiftest, arrived first. Mrs. Noah showed them where to stay. Two by two they came up into the Ark. The elephants followed, slow but sure, nodding their heads in rhythm. Two by two.

Two by two they came into the Ark. The tigers and the lions pulled in their claws, and licked their fur, and prowled the deck. Mrs. Noah was very busy. She directed traffic with her great wooden spoon. Jungle hippos followed their cousins, the mountain boars and country pigs. Two by two they all came.

Zebras, donkeys, ponies, horses trotted aboard, two by two by two. Two by two they came into the Ark. Leaping rabbits, jumping hares, Mr. and Mrs., two by two.

Two by two they came. Shaggy bears, for the first time meeting white bears who looked like snow, shuffled on, two by two. Two by two they came into the Ark. Lizards, toads, and crocodiles went two by two. The snakes were given plenty of room.

The apes, dromedaries, and giraffes, suspicious of sea voyages, were led in by the wives of Noah's sons, two by two. Two by two they came. Now the fishes were difficult, that was true. They had to be

9

carried by Ham and Shem and Japheth in wooden buckets, two by two.

Two by two they came into the Ark. The flying creatures flocked—eagles, parrots, sparrows, wrens, peacocks, walked aboard, two by two. Two by two. Even the snails were not forgotten.

Noah asked, "Everybody aboard?"

And Mrs. Noah used her wooden spoon to count every fish, beast, and fowl.

Suddenly blue water roared from the sky. The ocean swelled. All the seas burst forth. There came pouring, from all directions, torrents of rushing water. WHOOOSH! That rain rained for forty days and forty nights, and the earth filled with water.

Finally even the mountains disappeared. There was no sun and no moon. Just rain.

Now everybody on the Ark remained silent, trusting in Captain Noah, while the Ark floated out on the huge waters.

On the hundred-and-fiftieth morning, the Lord remembered Noah. And He sent a big wind to blow the waters away.

Noah leaned out the window in front, releasing a white dove. The white dove, after some hours, brought back a fresh olive twig. Green was some-

where on the earth again! From the Ark there was a great barking and roaring and whistling.

"The flood is going," cried Noah. "The Lord be praised." With joy the animals, birds, and fishes each sang in its own way to Him.

The Ark got stuck on a mountain top. So everybody had to climb down the rocky trail carefully.

For many months following, the earth lay as a swamp, with gigantic ferns and loud mosquitoes. Then the mud dried up at last. The earth was rich, and the world started growing.

The Lord gave Noah a better vineyard than before.

And some of the animals lived with him and Mrs. Noah.

SELAH

RUNAWAY JONAH

ONE pleasant noon, the farmer Jonah sat eating his lunch out of a clay dish, under a pomegranate tree. Bumblebees were buzzing. Spotted oxen roamed in the fields. Then, after Jonah was finished, he went to the well to fetch a drink of sweet water.

"JONAH!" a strange voice cried. Jonah peered down into the well, seeing nobody. "THIS IS THE LORD TALKING TO YOU!" Jonah trembled and listened. He wished he'd stayed under the tree.

14

"I WANT YOU TO DO SOMETHING FOR ME," continued the Lord. "GO TO NINEVEH, THAT WICKED CITY. TELL THEM I AM NOT PLEASED! GO NOW!"

In a twinkling, Jonah dropped the wooden cup into the deep well, and ran out of the fields to the port of Joppa, where he found a ship leaving for the city of Tarshish. There he thought he'd be safe. He was angry because the Lord picked on *him*.

But the Lord set up a terrible wind, hail was flung down from the sky, and the waves were mixed with thunder. The sailors worried that the ship might sink; so they threw much of their cargo overboard. Jonah was sleeping down in the hold, hidden in a corner.

The storm grew worse. High waves broke over the ship. The Lord wrote His name in lightning across the sky. "The Lord is displeased!" the sailors shouted. Some of them got on their knees and prayed, while the others rowed through the teeth of the gale. They feared the ship might break in two.

The ship's master went down into the hold to look for more things to throw overboard, and there he found Jonah. He shook him and cried, "How can you sleep through all this?" Jonah replied, "I put my hands over my ears."

15

Then Jonah went up on deck to see for himself. The storm was growing worse. Even the sea-foam was turning black. Soon Jonah admitted, "I am the one the Lord is after. Throw *me* into the sea!"

And this the sailors did, with tears in their eyes.

The angry waves grew calm immediately. And Jonah swam and swam and swam through the calm sea until suddenly he met a gray fish which opened its mouth and swallowed him.

Jonah stepped over the rows of sharp, bone-white teeth and sat on the fish's large gray tongue, which was stretched out like a rug. "This is the Lord's doing!" he moaned. "All because I wouldn't go to Nineveh!"

For ten minutes of every hour the fish rose to the surface to breathe. Then Jonah would stare out of the fish's mouth, wishing he were home.

Once, the fish leaped out of the water like a salmon and Jonah slithered down into the dark, wet belly and was unhappy.

There in the fish's belly Jonah stayed while the great fish swam and played among the dolphins and porpoises.

Then the fish left the sunny waters, wandering to the cold distant sea among the ice floes, the high ice cliffs, and the ice caves which cast blue and green shadows. Jonah had to dance the hornpipe to keep warm. At night he wrapped himself up in seaweed the fish had swallowed.

And Jonah spent much time praying to the Lord. The sailors on passing ships heard and were surprised. Loudly Jonah kept praying, till one day the Lord caused the fish to spit him out upon the shore. Jonah lay spread out on the sand like a starfish. "All right," Jonah said. "I'll go to Nineveh!" It took him three days to walk there.

And Jonah stood on the street corners of Nineveh preaching just as the Lord had asked him to. He shook his fists and told them the Lord was displeased. One by one they stopped to listen to him. They started to weep, so strong was his preaching. He kept shaking his fists and telling them many things. Soon the king and his subjects went around wearing sackcloth and ashes, ashamed of how they'd been acting in Nineveh.

However, Jonah was not satisfied. He was still very angry. He sat down in a weedy place on the edge of town, in the hot sun, and pouted. He believed the Lord ought to punish *everybody*. "It isn't fair," he growled and dug his fingers into the hot earth.

The Lord, then, was sorry for Jonah, and He grew a green plant which made a shade around him.

But on the next day He let the green plant die.

The hot sun beat again on Jonah's head. Jonah was angry. He called to the Lord, "Why don't you let me die too, like this plant?"

Then the cool night came. Birds sang in the bough of the juniper tree. And the Lord said:

"I AM SORRY FOR THAT PLANT. I AM SORRY FOR NINEVEH, WHICH I COULD KILL LIKE THE PLANT. BUT I WON'T. I AM ALSO SORRY FOR YOU, BECAUSE YOU TRIED TO RUN FROM ME. ARE YOU LISTENING, JONAH?"

"Oh Lord," Jonah answered, "I am listening! I will never run from you again." And Jonah never did.

Instead he became a bee-keeper and made honey.

SELAH

SINGING DAVID

IN the golden valley, people heard somebody up high, singing. "It is David, who keeps his father's sheep," said the washerwomen who were hanging their clothes over the thorn bushes. "A nice voice," nodded the poultrymen who were taking their fat geese to market in Bethlehem.

This David could leap across any brook, quick as an arrow, to chase a stray lamb.

21

And he liked to collect pebbles from the cool stream and shine them, holding them up to the sun.

And when the sheep got caught in the thorns he would untangle them.

This was his favorite song—

> *The Lord is a rock!*
> *And He will save*
> *David and his sheep!*
> *When they fall asleep!*
> *Lo ley!*
> *Lo ley!*

On a pillow of goat's hair, under a blanket of lamb's wool, David slept with one ear listening for sharp-toothed wolves.

Once he slew a prowling lion. And once he slew a bear. He cut off a paw from each to prove it.

Now, in those days, the Philistines were fighting against Israel with many soldiers and chariots. Israel's King Saul saw his people run off to hide in murky caves and dark thickets. Saul paced back and forth, getting more worried by the hour. "It is hard being king," he said. It certainly was. Saul was troubled.

So one afternoon David was brought from Bethlehem to sing for King Saul.

David plucked the strings of his harp and the tent was filled with his songs. This went on until he had sung all the songs he knew. Then Saul went back to his war, humming some tunes, and David returned to his sheep.

But one day David's father said, "Take to your brothers in Saul's army this parched corn, these loaves of bread, these cheeses. We'll find someone to watch the sheep while you are gone."

David took some of his pebble collection along for luck. Off he went, past the broken fig trees and palm trees, through thick dust, through the sound of whizzing arrows, until he found his brothers.

David's brothers' names were Eliab, Abinadab, and Shammah. Eliab was the oldest.

Now among the Philistines the champion was a hairy giant whose name was Goliath. He wore thick brass armor that no spear could pierce. At the top of the tallest hill Goliath stood, rooted like a great oak tree.

He shouted, *"Puny Israel! If you dare! Send forth one man against me! Let who wins be called the winner of this battle between us!"*

However, there was no one among Israel's soldiers who dared to fight a giant. So everybody waited and worried.

24

It was Eliab, his brother, who teased David, saying, "Why don't you try? Do you suppose you are brave enough?" Eliab laughed; but David sat down and thought and thought about it.

David said to himself, "The Lord saved me from the paw of the lion and the paw of the bear. Maybe he will save me from Goliath." So he rubbed both paws for luck, and declared he would do it. King Saul came hurrying, saying, "You are just a boy. You had better go home."

Nevertheless, David insisted. Therefore they dressed him in heavy armor, and put on him a brass helmet, and gave him a bronze sword.

"Listen," David said, "I can't move with all these things on." So he took them off and carried with him only his shepherd's staff, a handful of pebbles, and a little sling. Then he climbed up the tall hill on which Goliath stood. To keep his courage up, he sang to himself one of his favorite songs.

Some ravens cawed.

The red sun was sinking in the sky.

Goliath was angry to see a boy dare to fight him, and raised one great foot in the air, ready to take a step. David swiftly stuck a pebble in his sling and shot it. SMACK! It hit the giant full in the forehead.

Off-balance, he went tumbling off the hill with a weighty, rolling, clanking crash! Headfirst, his body made a hole in the ground, and only his boots stuck out of it.

Saul's soldiers shouted!

Philistines scattered like rabbits.

Joyously David sang another song—giving praise to the Lord! Then he was carried on a platform of shields to greet King Saul. Everybody rushed out from the houses, the bushes, and the caves in which they'd been hiding, and they danced upon the battleground, shaking tambourines!

Above Israel, all that night, hung the bright October moon.

SELAH

LITTLE JOSEPH

OLD Jacob had twelve sons; of them, Benjamin was the youngest. The mother, whose name was Rachel, called him Benoni, and then she shut her eyes and died. But Old Jacob liked to call him Benjamin.

The son whom Old Jacob loved best was the next-to-youngest, Little Joseph. He loved him so much that with his own hands he stitched for him a patchwork cloak of many colors. Little Joseph liked to strut around showing this off to his older brothers. Of course the brothers grew jealous.

Once Little Joseph lay down and had a dream. The dream went like this:

He was in a field with his brothers, binding sheaves of wheat, and his sheaf arose and stood upright. His brothers' sheaves stood around it, bowing.

Soon after, Little Joseph had another dream, which went like this:

The sun, the moon, and the stars in the heavens were dazzled by him in his many-colored cloak.

Little Joseph told his brothers. They asked, "What do these dreams mean? Must we bow down to you, too? Must we be dazzled by you?" Then they walked out into the fields, grumbling to each other, "He is getting a big head."

One day, Old Jacob said, "Your brothers are somewhere with their flocks, and soon it will be time for supper. Can you go find them?"

Little Joseph, who was sitting with Benjamin, the baby, said, "I will find them, Father." So he went off, wearing his rainbow cloak that could be seen a mile away, at least. When his brothers saw him coming they ducked in the bushes. When Little Joseph arrived, they jumped out and tore off the cloak and tossed him into a big hole in the ground.

"Let's keep him there," one of them suggested. They all thought that was a very good idea.

After a while there came along a company of merchants, bearing rare spices and oils, on its way to Egypt. Then Little Joseph's brothers said to each other, "Why don't we sell the booby instead of leaving him down in that hole?" So they did, and they got two silver coins each for him.

Then they tore up the beautiful cloak and took it back to Old Jacob, saying, "Look at this! This is all that is left of our brother, who must have been eaten by wolves."

Old Jacob moaned and went right away and fixed a grave, putting in it the shreds of Little Joseph's cloak. He heaped the grave with many flowers and wept over it many long days.

Meanwhile, Little Joseph was carried off to Egypt and put on a flat barge going up the Nile.

He was sold to Potiphar, captain of the Pharaoh's guard and the owner of a large plantation. Potiphar liked Little Joseph at once and made him over-seer of his plantation, on which grew barley and wheat.

Little Joseph watched over the farm well; and every morning he would rise, before the rooster's crowing, to watch the morning bread being baked. But one morning Potiphar's wife got angry with Little Joseph and had her husband throw him into a black prison. Little Joseph was getting to like life on the plantation, and was sad to leave it.

However, he was locked up in a dungeon cell with the Pharaoh's own butler and baker, who had displeased the Pharaoh. Little Joseph and the Butler and the Baker became friends. When the Butler and the Baker had bad dreams, Little Joseph sat down with them and tried to tell the dreams' meanings. He grew very skilled at it.

One night the Butler had a dream about three grapevines. And he came to Little Joseph and told him. Little Joseph thought it over.

He said, "This means in three days the Pharaoh is going to let you out of prison and give you your job again. That is what it means to me." Then he added, "If it goes well with you, please tell the Pharaoh about me, because I'd like to get out of here, too."

The same night the Baker also had a dream, and his was about three white baskets. So he came to Little Joseph and told him. And Little Joseph thought it over.

"TEMPLE ISRAEL"

He said, "This means—poor fellow—if I am right —in three days you are going to die. I'm sorry." Then they went to sleep again.

Well, it happened, in three days, that the Pharaoh pardoned the Butler and hanged the Baker. Then Little Joseph was alone in the dungeon cell.

Now the Pharaoh was troubled with strange dreams also. One night he had two. The first of them was about seven very lean cows chasing seven very fat cows. The second one was about seven very lean ears of corn chasing seven very fat ears of corn.

The Pharaoh asked all his court magicians what these dreams could mean. Yet they were unable to tell him, no matter what kind of magic they tried with bats' wings and scorpion shells and old dry bones.

Finally the Butler, who brought the Pharaoh a cup of wine, remembered how clever Little Joseph was. He said, "*He* might know." So a gong was immediately struck and Little Joseph was brought from prison.

Little Joseph sat on a tiny stool at the Pharaoh of Egypt's feet. He shut his eyes and seemed to go into a trance.

He said, "Seven fat cows, seven fat ears of corn . . . means Egypt will have seven fat years. Seven lean cows, seven lean ears of corn . . . means Egypt will have seven lean years. So, during the seven fat years you'd better put away enough corn and meat to feed you during the seven lean years."

Then Little Joseph opened his eyes. The Pharaoh was so impressed that he made Little Joseph governor of Egypt and its surrounding lands.

It happened just as Little Joseph told Pharaoh. After the seven fat years there were very lean years, and the crops stopped growing.

After two years of the seven lean had passed, Little Joseph's ten older brothers came riding into Egypt on donkeys to buy some corn.

The brothers were brought into the governor's gleaming halls. They did not recognize Little Joseph in his new, splendid robes. He held a gold stick.

His ten brothers bowed down low in front of him till their noses touched the floor. Then Little Joseph remembered his dreams that had made them angry, and smiled. He said to them in a loud voice, "You look like spies to me—who have come to see how poor Egypt is!"

They wailed and protested, "No, great governor! That isn't true! We've only come to buy a bit of corn for ourselves, and for our old father, and our littlest brother! We swear!"

"You are spies," Little Joseph insisted, banging his gold stick on the floor. They pleaded again. "Then, if you're *not* spies, you may take some corn in these sacks. But—to prove the truth of your word, leave one of you behind. And bring back to me this littlest brother!" He banged again his gold stick on the floor.

The ten brothers shuddered, and trembled for their lives. Yet they agreed to do it, because they had to. They chose lots and Simeon lost, so he was locked up in a dungeon. However, as soon as the nine of them left, Little Joseph had some poppy-seed cake sent down to Simeon.

When the brothers reached home, they opened their cloth sacks and found among the corn all the money they had paid—returned!

Old Jacob kneeled down and prayed. He said at last, "This may be a mistake. All I know is this, I have lost Little Joseph. Now I have lost Simeon, too. I will not lose my Benjamin as well!" And he went out and sat at Little Joseph's grave, weeping.

However, all too soon, the corn was eaten up. It was necessary to go back to Egypt.

Old Jacob fretted, and then he said, "Then you must go, or we will starve. Take Benjamin with you. But take, besides, double the amount of gold, so they do not say you were stealing. Take also, to this governor, baskets of fruit; take almonds and spices and pistachio nuts. Take honey. Perhaps then he will not keep Benjamin, who is just a small boy." So they gathered these things, and went out the door. Old Jacob watched them go.

Once again ten brothers rode to Egypt. They trembled with fear during the whole hot journey. Hungry buzzards flew over their heads.

When they arrived, they sent to the governor the gold and the fruit and almonds and spices and pistachio nuts. They came to the governor's halls with their littlest brother, Benjamin. How afraid they were!

Little Joseph sat on his throne and didn't speak. Instead he said, "Take them to my house. Give them a dinner of corn and bread and meat." He released Simeon from prison. He next had Benjamin dressed in purple linen and embroidered slippers. While they were eating he had their gold, again, stuffed into their sacks with the corn. And he hid in Benjamin's sack a small silver cup.

Then that was all. He let them go home, the eleven brothers. They were beginning to believe in their happy fortune—when suddenly, in the night, lighted torches appeared. Soldiers on swift horses caught up with them and searched through every sack. At the bottom of Benjamin's was found the silver cup.

So, in the middle of the night, they were brought back to Little Joseph.

Little Joseph thumped his gold stick on the floor. "Is this how you repay my kindness?" he shouted. "By stealing from me what is MINE?"

They grew more frightened than before. They quaked, and fell on their knees, and yelled for mercy. They were sure he was going to throw them to the crocodiles.

Instead, the governor ordered his guards to leave the room. He stood alone in his brilliant robes among his brothers. "Don't you know what is truly mine?" he asked, throwing wide his arms. Then he named them, one after the other, Reuben, and Simeon, and every one—including the smallest, Benjamin.

They looked at him, still dazzled by his robes.

40

He hugged them one by one, and whispered into each ear, "I'm Little Joseph."

For he loved them. Wildly they rushed about the place weeping and tearing their own clothes into rags, with shame.

Then Little Joseph gathered all his eleven brothers around him.

He said, "If you did not do what you did, we would probably be dead, since the crops are not growing. But because I am governor there is plenty for us to eat. So you must come and live with me."

And he sent away for Old Jacob, and they all lived together in Egypt in wind and rain and yellow sun.

SELAH

42

Temple Israel
Library
Minneapolis, Minn.

יהי אור

LET THERE BE LIGHT

In honor of
Confirmation:
Robert Greenberg
by
Mr. & Mrs. A. H. Fremland